Computer BASICS

BOOK 1

Jill Jesson

Hi, my name is Dex. We're going to help you develop your computer skills.

Hi, my name is Data. Check out our website at: www.letts-education.com

Contents

This book has been written for use with Microsoft Office 2000. The ideas suggested will also work well, with a few minor amendments, using many other programs including Microsoft Works, ClarisWorks, and AppleWorks on Apple machines. (see inside back cover for more details).

Young children may need help to start, save and print their work.

The first time your child uses this book you may need to help them learn each new skill. They will soon be able to practise by themselves.

To start

▶ Click on **Start**. Go up to **Programs**.

▶ Select one of the Microsoft Office icons.

From the Programs menu you can

▶ Click on   **Microsoft Word**   Word Processor

   Microsoft Access   Database

   Microsoft Excel   Spreadsheet

▶ These icons show which type of document you need. They appear immediately before the title of each page.

WP	Word Processing	WP D	Drawing in Word Processing
SS	Spreadsheet	P	Paint Document
CD	CD-ROM	Cal	Calculator

In Word check the Drawing toolbar is visible. Go to View, click Toolbars and tick Drawing.

To type

▶ Everything that should be typed onto the computer is highlighted, to make it easy to follow.

To draw

▶ Use drawing tools directly onto the page.

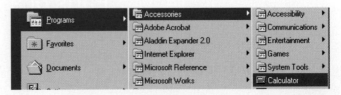

To use the calculator or Microsoft Paint

▶ Open the calculator or Microsoft Paint from the Accessories menu.

Saving

▶ Get into the habit of saving your work soon after starting a new document – then you will not lose it accidentally.

To save

▶ Click on File .

▶ Click on Save .

▶ Save in My Documents.

Each person in the family could have their own folder in My Documents.

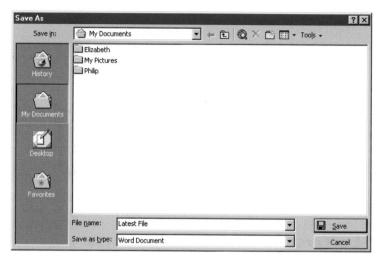

New work

▶ There are many ideas to try on each page.

▶ Start a new document for special ideas you want to keep.

Common problems

▶ To stop unwanted capitals appearing, click Tools , AutoCorrect... and remove ticks from Capitalize boxes.

▶ Insert key Insert allows you to either insert new letters or write over old ones.
   If OVR is showing, tap the Insert key Insert once to remove it.

Mistakes

▶ To undo a mistake hold Ctrl and tap Z once.

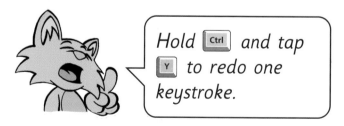

Hold Ctrl and tap Y to redo one keystroke.

Mouse speed

▶ You need to double-click the mouse quite fast.

▶ If you can't click fast enough you can slow the speed required.

▶ To do this, alter the mouse setting in Control Panel .

Mouse

To select text

▶ Text must be selected and highlighted before it can be altered. To select it you can double-click on a word, triple-click on a line, or click and drag across a whole block of text.

Tapping a key puts a letter or a number on the screen.

Tapping the `Backspace ←` key rubs it out.

Work can be saved.

Word processing

To start, click here.

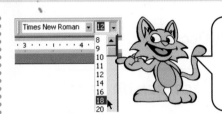

Click here to start in size 18.

Letters

▶ Tap a letter once.

▶ Press `←Enter`.

▶ Tap another letter three times.

▶ Press `←Enter`.

▶ Tap letters and `←Enter` to make a pattern.

q

www

mmmm

Alphabet

▶ Type the alphabet.

abcdefghijklmnopqrstuvwxyz

If you make a mistake, tap the `Backspace ←` key.

Name

▶ Type your name. Tap `Backspace ←` to rub it out.

▶ Type other names.

▶ Type words you know.

▶ Type the numbers 1 to 9.

Rover
Dad
Mum
Gran

Quick type

▶ Keep score:

▶ How many times can you type your name in one minute?

▶ Write your scores here.

first go	
second go	
third go	

▶ Ask someone else to try. Who wins?

How long does it take you to type the alphabet?

Learn to save

▶ When you have finished your typing click File .

▶ Click Save .

▶ Double-click My Documents.

▶ Type a name for your work.

Type a name for your work here. If you want your own folder click on and type your name.

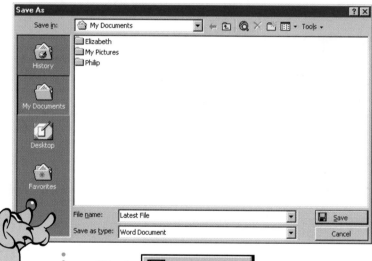

▶ Click Save .

▶ This saves your work into the folder called Documents.

Letter patterns

▶ Carry on typing on your page.

▶ Hold a letter down and see what happens at the end of a line.

ggggggggggggggggggggggggg ggggg

▶ Make patterns with lines of letters.

pbpbpbpbp   sosososos

Click the Close Window box ✕ to finish.

5

To type one capital letter hold ⬆Shift and tap the letter.

To type many capital letters press Caps Lock and tap the letters.

Pressing Caps Lock saves you holding ⬆Shift down.

Shift key

▶ Tap a letter once.   a

▶ Hold ⬆Shift and tap it again.   A

▶ Tap another letter twice.   oo

▶ Hold ⬆Shift and tap it again.   OO

You need to press ↵Enter *to start a new line.*

On some computers the key is called Return.

▶ Make a pattern with capital and small letters.

aAaAaAaAaAa

BbBbBbBb

wWwW

IiIi

Caps Lock key

▶ Press Caps Lock and write your name in capitals.

TIM JANE

▶ Press Caps Lock again and write your name.

tim jane

▶ Type this:

HELP me HELP me HELP me

DING dong DING dong

BIG little HUGE small

GIANT tiny ELEPHANT mouse

Shift and numbers

▶ Hold ⬆Shift and tap the numbers 1 to 10.

▶ Tap Caps Lock and tap the numbers again.

▶ What happens on the screen?

!@#$%^&*()12345678910

Start with a capital

▶ Names start with capital letters.

▶ Use [⇧ Shift] to start your name.

   Julia   David

▶ Type other names. Give each name a capital letter.

▶ Type these words:

   Dex Data London England

▶ Type your name and address.

Miss Witch

Mint House

Toffee Lane

Sugar Town

FAIRYLAND

Writing paper patterns

▶ Make your own writing paper.

▶ Do a pattern at the top and bottom.

XXXXXXXXXXXXXXXXXXXXXXXXXXXXXXX

SSssSSssSSssSSssSSssSSssSSssSSssSSssSSss

Big House
Little Lane
Tiny Town

PqPqPqPqPqPqPqPqPqPqPqPqPqPqPqPqPqPqPqP

OOOoooOOOoooOOOoooOOOoooOOOoooOOOooo

Make a spare line by tapping [⏎ Enter] twice.

▶ Save your letter in your folder.

I made these patterns using the Shift key [⇧ Shift].

%%*%*%*%*%*%*%*%*%*

£\$£\$£\$£\$£\$£\$£\$£\$£\$£\$£\$£\$£\$£\$£\$

&+&+&+&+&+&+&+&+&+&+

!!"!!"!!"!!"!!"!!"!!"!!"!!"!!"!!

(((^^^)))(((^^^)))(((^^^)))(((^^^)))

@?@?@?@?@?@?@?@?@?@?

^+^+^+^+^+^+^+^+^+^+^+^+^+^+^

><<>><<>><<>><<>><<>><

{\$} {\$} {\$} {\$} {\$} {\$} {\$} {\$} {\$}

~~~~~~~~~~~~~~~~~~~~~~~~

Using both hands to type is quicker than one.

To put spaces between words tap on the space bar.

Use your thumbs to tap the space bar.

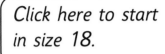

Click here to start in size 18.

▶ Use your right hand for keys on the right of the keyboard.

▶ Use your left hand for keys on the left side.

One hand

▶ With your right hand type:

LIP   PILL   PIN

▶ With your left hand type:

WAS   SAD   TAR

Both hands

▶ Use both hands to type:

PAM   SOS   POD

Type more words using both hands.

Spaces

▶ Use your thumbs to tap the space bar.

▶ Type: P space Q space O space W space L space A space M space Z

▶ Type patterns of letters and spaces.

C ZZ MMM LLLL   TTTTT

Put one space here

put two spaces here

put three spaces here ...

Patterns

▶ Type patterns of words and spaces.

DRIP   DRIP

DRI

P

Don't forget to tap `←Enter` *for a new line.*

A rhyme

▶ Type these words and spaces.

Dex is a clever cat.

Data is a smart mouse.

▶ Try this cat and mouse rhyme.

Data mouse Data mouse where have you been?

I've been to London to look at the queen.

Data mouse Data mouse what did you do there?

I frightened a little cat under her chair.

Not me – you silly.

Poster

▶ Start a new page.

Click here.

📄 Document4 - Micros

File Edit View Insert

New Blank Document

▶ Change the font size to 48.

▶ Make a poster for your room.

▶ Use spaces to spread the words out.

PRIVATE

Keep Out   Keep Out

SECRET   SPACE

PLEASE KNOCK

Genius at work

MY

DEN

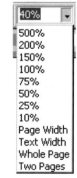

40%

500%
200%
150%
100%
75%
50%
25%
10%
Page Width
Text Width
Whole Page
Two Pages

Click ▾. *Click on* Whole Page *to help you plan your poster.*

▶ Save and print your poster.

Move the mouse to move a pointer on the screen.
The pointer can be an arrow ⃕ or an I bar Ⅰ.
Letters can be coloured and moved.

The mouse

▶ Start with a new document.

▶ Use the mouse to move the pointer Ⅰ around the screen.

▶ Move it to the edge of the screen. It will change to an arrow ⃕.

▶ Move the arrow ⃕ around the screen.

▶ Try not to let the pointer change its shape.

Use the pointer to point at the icons on the screen. Read their labels.

Drawing Toolbar

▶ Click `View` and click `Toolbars`.

▶ Click `Drawing`.

A tick will show that the Drawing Toolbar is open.

✔ Drawing

▶ Click the Text box icon `▤`.

▶ Type a letter in the text box and then click on the document.

*Click arrow ▾ next to 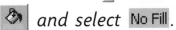 and select `No Fill`.
Click arrow ▾ next to 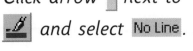 and select `No Line`.*

▶ Click `▤` again.

▶ Click in a different part of the document.

▶ Type different letters all over the screen.

Drawing patterns

▶ Make patterns of letters like this:

```
X       X
  X   X
    X
  X   X
X       X
```

▶ Make a pattern with the first letter of your name:

```
DDD
D   D
D     D
D   D
DDD
```

▶ Make a pattern like this:

OoOoOoOoOoOoOoOoOoOoOoOo

or this:

PjPjPjPjPjPjPjPjPjPjPjPjPjPjPj

▶ Click after each letter and `Backspace ←` to rub it out.

Dragging patterns

▶ Make a pattern like this in a single text box.

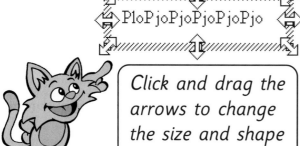

Click and drag the arrows to change the size and shape of the text box.

▶ When the cursor looks like this ⊹ click and drag the box around the screen.

▶ Make each pattern a different colour.

XXXXXXXXXXXXXXXXX
OoOoOoOoOoOoOoOoOoOoOoOoO
ssssSSSSssss   HIHIHIHIHI
     PjoPjoPjoPjoPjo
     ckckckckckckckckckc

Select some text. Click arrow ▾ next to **A** *and make your letters different colours.*

Make a picture from patterns

BBBBBBBBBB
bbbbbbbbbbbbbbbb

YY   OO   OO   YY
CCC   I   CCC
uuy   I   yuu
  zz   L---J   zz
    boeooeooeod
    eoeoeoeoe

▶ Click outside the selected window.

▶ You are now in the word processing document again.

▶ Click on a text box to change it.

Zoom for a better view

▶ Click ▾ to see the Whole Page .

▶ Drag the handles to resize the text box.

XXXXXXXXXXXXXXXXXX
OoOoOoOoOoOoOoOoOoOoOoOoO
ssssSSSSssss   HIHIHIHIHI
PjoPjoPjoPjoPjo
ckck ckckckckckckckckc
XXXXXXXXXXX

Drag this handle to make it wider.

Drag this handle to make it longer.

11

You can use tools to draw shapes.

Shapes can be changed by dragging their handles.

Shapes can be copied.

Boxes

▶ Click the Rectangle tool .

▶ The pointer changes to a +.

▶ Click on the page and drag the + to make a rectangle.

Change the shape

▶ Click outside the shape to lose the handles.

▶ Click inside the shape to see its handles.

▶ Drag the shape around the screen.

▶ Drag the handles to change the shape.

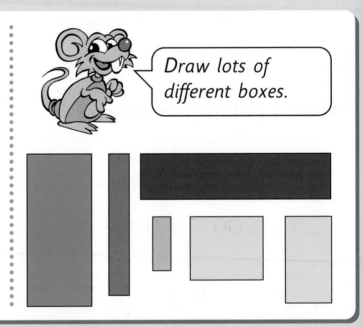

Draw lots of different boxes.

Ovals

▶ Draw an oval. Use the Oval tool.

▶ Move it around the screen.

▶ Draw more ovals.

▶ Change their size and shape.

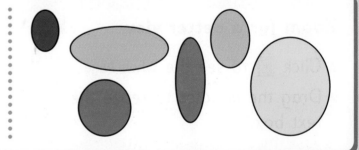

AutoShapes

▶ Draw shapes in the same way using the AutoShapes ▾ menu.

Colour your shapes

▶ Click on a shape you have drawn.

▶ Click 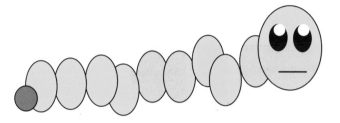 to colour its edge.

▶ Click 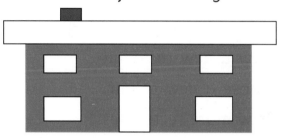 to colour all of the shape.

Pictures from shapes

▶ Draw animals from circles.

▶ Make houses from rectangles.

Copy shapes

▶ To copy a shape:

  1 Click the shape.

  2 Click Copy 🗎.

  3 Click Paste 📋.

  4 Drag the copy to where you want it.

▶ Copy rectangles to make trucks.

▶ Copy circles to make wheels.

Combine shapes

▶ Make pictures from different shapes.

▶ Use them to make your own colouring book.

Shapes can be coloured or patterned.

Coloured rectangles

▶ Draw a rectangle.

▶ Colour the line.

▶ Fill with colour.

▶ Drag it around the screen.

Smaller and larger rectangles

▶ Draw a new rectangle.

▶ Choose a new colour.

▶ Draw more rectangles.

▶ Use the handles to change their shapes.

▶ Copy and Paste these shapes.

Coloured ovals

▶ Use the Oval tool ⬭ to draw a circle.

Change the border colour by clicking 🖌▾.

▶ Click 🪣▾ and select Fill Effects....

▶ Click Pattern.

▶ Click a pattern you like.

▶ Click OK.

▶ Click ☰ and choose a thick line.

▶ Click 🖌▾ and select Patterned Lines....

▶ Click a pattern you like.

▶ Copy these shapes.

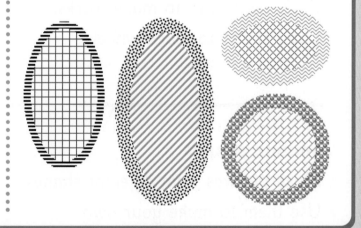

Overlaying shapes

▶ Draw and colour another shape.

▶ Add a pattern.

▶ Drag it over some of the other shapes to make a picture.

Freeform

▶ Click AutoShapes ▾ and click Lines.

▶ Click the Freeform tool ⌂.

▶ Click in different places on the screen.

▶ Click twice to finish the shape.

▶ Colour the line.

▶ Fill with colour.

▶ Change the shapes using their handles.

Click on this and drag it to change the shape.

Computer pencils

▶ Click AutoShapes ▾ and click Lines.

▶ Click the ✎ tool.

▶ Press the mouse button to see the pencil ✐.

▶ Keep the mouse button pressed and scribble a shape.

▶ Colour the line.

▶ Fill with colour.

▶ Give it a pattern.

▶ Write your name with the pencil.

▶ Print your pictures and put them on your wall.

Group, zoom and save

▶ Use the pointer ▱ to drag a rectangle around your picture.

▶ Click Draw ▾ and click Group.

▶ Add a title using a text box.

▶ Click File and Save to your folder.

Pull the handles to stretch the picture. Pull this handle to make it longer.

Pull this to make it wider.

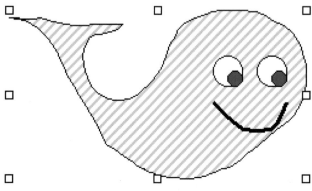

Lines and shape edges can be altered in thickness.
Lines and borders can be coloured or patterned.

Lines

▶ Select the Line tool ◹.

The pointer ⬉ changes to a +.

▶ Click and drag the mouse.

▶ Make lines all over the screen.

▶ Click a line.

▶ Backspace to rub it out.

▶ Rub out all the lines.

Click here to close.

Line colour

▶ Draw a line.

▶ Click on  and choose a colour.

▶ Draw another line.

▶ Click on a different colour.

▶ Draw lines in different colours all over the screen.

When the line has got small squares (handles) at each end you can change its colour.

Thick and thin lines

▶ Draw a line.

▶ Click on Line Style icon to change thickness. ☰

▶ Click on 6 point.

▶ Draw another line and change it using Dash Style icon. ▦

▶ Experiment with Arrow Styles. ⇄

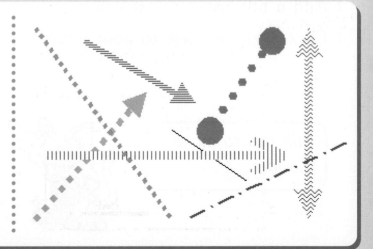

Charts

▶ Make a homework chart.

▶ Draw lines and boxes on the screen like this:

Look at page 12 to see how to draw boxes. Click on their edges and change the style and colour.

Don't select the  tool or your boxes will fill with colour.

▶ Print the page.

▶ Write a spelling to learn on each line.

▶ Put a sum to learn in each box.

Pictures

▶ Make pictures like these.

I drew these from lines and circles.

▶ Double-click the Line icon to draw lots of lines the same.

Displays

▶ Put your charts and pictures on the wall.

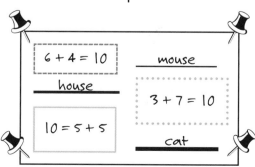

6 + 4 = 10

mouse

house

3 + 7 = 10

10 = 5 + 5

cat

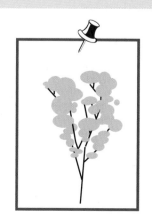

Data is information.

Data can be numbers, writing or pictures.

Record card

▶ Start with size 24 font.

▶ Write your name.

▶ Put in ten spaces.

▶ Write your age.

▶ Put in ten more spaces.

▶ Draw a picture of yourself.

Add a picture

I used Oval tool for the face and eyes, and Scribble tool for the hair, nose and smile.

Group your picture. See page 15 if you get stuck.

Data fields

James   10

▶ Your record has 3 fields:
  NAME AGE PICTURE

▶ Do this for each person in your family.

▶ Tap **↵Enter** four times to leave space.

▶ Save the family database in your folder.

Click **▾** *to see*
Whole Page ▾

James   10

Mum   36

Dad   38

Dragging around

▶ Select and drag the names and faces around the screen.

▶ Ask someone to unjumble them.

Friends' database

▶ Make a database about your friends.

▶ Put 'boy' or 'girl' on each record. (This is another field.)

It now has four fields.

Boy   Ian   7

Girl   Sarah   8

Boy   Imran   7

Toy database

▶ Make a toy database.

▶ On each record put:
TOY
MATERIAL
FROM

▶ Add a picture.

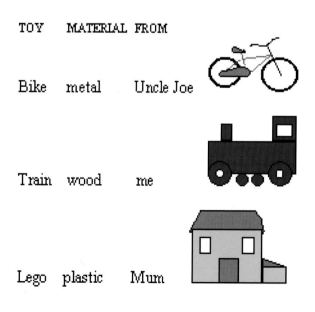

TOY	MATERIAL	FROM
Bike	metal	Uncle Joe
Train	wood	me
Lego	plastic	Mum

Starting Spreadsheets

Spreadsheets store information.

They have boxes called cells.

Cells are arranged in rows and columns.

Spreadsheets can make graphs.

Starting a spreadsheet

▶ Open a spreadsheet.

You click this icon on the Office toolbar.

▶ Use the mouse to click the pointer ✛ in different cells.

▶ Click and drag across cells beside each other. This is a row.

▶ Click and drag across cells below each other. This is a column.

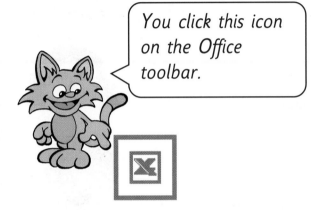

Cells

▶ The rows are numbered 1,2,3,4, etc.

▶ The columns are labelled A,B,C,D, etc.

▶ Click in cell 1A, click in 3B, click in 5D.

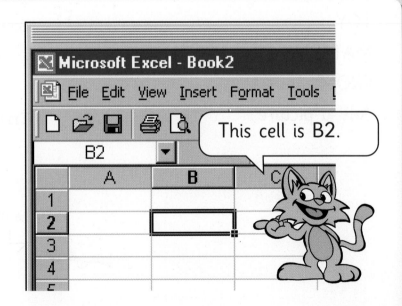

This cell is B2.

Selecting cells

▶ Click in 1 A. Type the number 1.
▶ Click in 2 A. Type 2.
▶ Click in 3 A. Type 3.
▶ Click in 4 A. Type 4.
▶ Click in 5 A. Type 5.

Drag across the cells to select them.

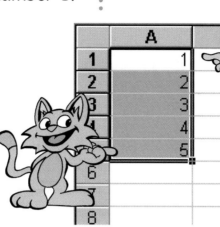

This cell stays clear to show you where you started.

▶ Click on the Graph button 📊 at the top of the screen.

▶ Select a graph type and click **Finish**.

Graphs

▶ Click 🗋 for a new document.

▶ In column A type names of people you know.

▶ In column B type their ages.

▶ Click and drag across all the cells.

	A	B	C
1	Lee	9	
2	Sue	8	
3	Imran	8	
4	Dave	6	
5	Ralph	9	
6	Ricky	7	
7	Dan	8	
8	Shazia	7	
9	Laura	8	
10	Liz	12	
11			
12			

▶ Click 📊.
▶ Select a graph type.
▶ Click **Finish**.

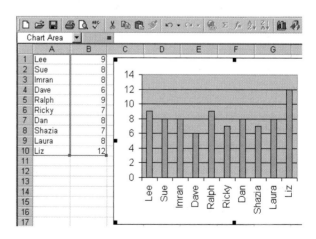

Drag down and across.

Scroll bars can be used to see all of a document.
Information (data) can be shown as pictograms.

Choose size 48 from here.

Lists

- On your word processor page tap 1. Press [↵Enter].
- Tap 2 and press [↵Enter].
- Tap 3 and press [↵Enter].
- Stop at 9.

Up and down

- Click here [▲] to go up.
- Click here [▼] to go down.

Side to side

- Click here [▶] to go right.
- Click here [◀] to go left.
- Use [Backspace ←] to make the numbers disappear.

Fonts

- Click the font box [Times New Roman ▼] to see the fonts.
- Click here [▼] to go up and down the list.
- Choose a picture font.

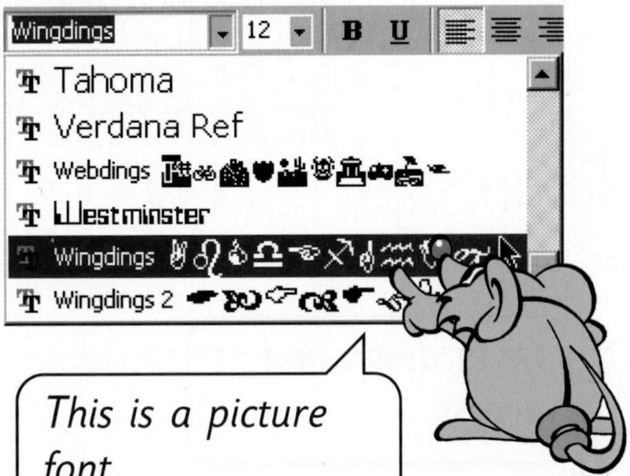

This is a picture font.

- Tap the keys to make pictures.
- Put a space after each picture.

If you forget a space, click the pointer between the pictures and tap the space bar.

- Drag across a picture. It will go black.
- Drag the picture to a new space.
- Move the pictures around the page.

Picture this

▶ Type your name in pictures.

▶ Type a friend's name.

▶ Type Dex.

▶ Type Data.

▶ Whose name is the longest?

Pictogram

▶ Count the lights in your house.

▶ Write the answers here.

sitting room	
kitchen	
my bedroom	
bathroom	

▶ Make a pictogram chart.

▶ Start a new page with size 36 font.

▶ Tap L for each light in the sitting room.

▶ Tap the space bar ten times.

▶ Type sitting room.

▶ Tap ⏎Enter.

▶ Do the same for the other rooms.

LLLL	sitting room
LLLLLL	kitchen
LLL	my bedroom
LLL	bathroom

▶ Which room has the most lights?

▶ How many lights are there altogether?

Animal pictogram

▶ Count these animals.

▶ Make a pictogram to show how many of each there are.

birds	bbbbbbb
cats	
mice	
dog	

23

Calculators can add and subtract.
They can be used to check sums.

Open calculator

Open the calculator from the Accessories menu.

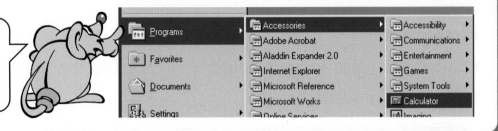

Adding patterns

▶ Click [1] on the calculator.

▶ Click [+] on the calculator.

▶ Click [1] on the calculator.

▶ Click [=] on the calculator.

$$1 + 1 = 2$$

▶ Click [1] click [+] click [2]

click [=] $1 + 2 = 3$

▶ Click [1] click [+] click [3]

click [=] $1 + 3 = 4$

▶ Click [1] click [+] click [4]

click [=] $1 + 4 = 5$

▶ Do this for other numbers. What is the pattern?

Click [C] to start each new sum.

Simple sums

▶ Do these sums on the calculator.

▶ Write the answers here:

$2 + 3 =$ ☐ $7 + 4 =$ ☐

$4 + 2 =$ ☐ $3 + 8 =$ ☐

▶ Now add 3 numbers.

$1 + 2 + 3 =$ ☐

$3 + 4 + 2 =$ ☐

$6 + 2 + 5 =$ ☐

Subtract

▶ Use the calculator to take away a number.

▶ Click [-] to take away.

▶ Write the answers here.

6 – 2 = ☐

5 – 1 = ☐

9 – 6 = ☐

8 – 4 = ☐

Two digits

▶ For a two-digit number click both digits.

A number is made of digits.

12 + 5 = ☐

5 + 10 = ☐

10 – 5 = ☐

21 – 11 = ☐

▶ Make up sums of your own.

Practice

▶ Use buttons or sweets to do these sums.

▶ Write the answers on paper.

▶ Use the calculator to check your answers.

▶ Use the calculator to check sums you do in your head.

6 + 10 = ☐   10 + 6 = ☐

5 + 9 = ☐   8 + 8 = ☐

10 – 6 = ☐   12 – 6 = ☐

20 – 5 = ☐   20 – 10 = ☐

I use a calculator to check my homework.

Using a CD-ROM to Find Out About Animals

Use a CD-ROM to find out about animals.
The CD-ROM Encarta contains information and pictures.

Getting started

▶ Put the Encarta disc in the drive.

▶ Type cat in the `Find` box.

`Find` `cat` `Home`

▶ Tap `↵Enter`.

▶ Click `Cat` in the list.

▶ Click Cat Family .

Cat C

`article`

Cat. *See* Cat, Domestic; Cat Family.

Moving around

▶ Use the arrows `←` `→` to move across the screen.

▶ Put the pointer on each picture and read the label.

▶ How many cats are there on this screen?

▶ There are ☐ cat pictures on this screen.

The white arrow next to `Home` *gets you back to the main cat screen.*

Sounds and movies

▶ Click the last picture to see the cheetah run.

▶ Click the jaguar to hear it roar.

More videos

▶ Click the white arrow `←` to go back to the index.

▶ Click on `Cat, Domestic`.

▶ Click on `multimedia`.

▶ Find this icon `│Landing on Four Feet`.

▶ Click it to see the video.

Dogs

▶ In the **Find** box type dog.

▶ Tap **↵Enter**.

▶ Click **Dog, Domestic** .

▶ Draw the dog you like best here.

Birds

▶ Look up bird.

▶ Which bird song do you like best?

Use a CD-ROM to find out about places (the UK)

▶ Type the name of each country in the **Find** box.

> *Click on the map and find the red star ★. This is the capital.*

ENGLAND

▶ Capital city (by ★): _____

▶ Click on **Rievaulx Abbey** .
Use the arrows to see all around it.

▶ What is this?

_____

NORTHERN IRELAND

▶ Capital city: _____

▶ Largest lake: _____

▶ What is this?

_____

SCOTLAND

▶ Capital city: _____

▶ Click **Highland Fling of Scotland** to hear this dance.

▶ What is this?

_____

WALES

▶ Capital city: _____

▶ Click on **▲Snowdon** .

▶ Click on **Go to Article...** .

▶ What is Snowdon? _____

▶ Explore Wales.

Use skills from this book to make a Family and Friends Book.

Drawing

- Start a new Word page.
- Write your NAME in CAPITALS.
- Write your age in numbers.
- Make a coloured frame for a picture.
- Print the record and draw your picture in the frame.

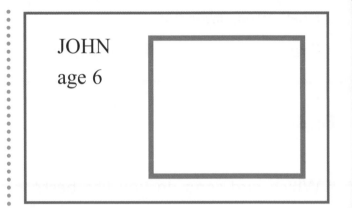

Word processor

- Choose a big font.
- List the things you like.
- Make a list of things you don't like.
- Print and stick both pages in a scrapbook.
- Do the same for your family and friends.

Book cover

- Open another Word page to make a cover for your book.
- Draw a shape first.
- Then add your title in a big font size.
- Click ▾ to see the Whole Page.
- Use the handles to make it bigger.

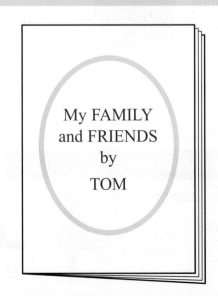

Spreadsheet

▶ Use a spreadsheet (see page 20).

▶ Add a graph to show the ages of the people in your book.

Family list

▶ Use the word processor.

▶ List the people in your family.

▶ Put their names in a frame.

> Me
> Mum
> Dad
> Tim, the goldfish
> Sara
> Liz
> Gran

Friends' list

▶ Build a wall with the names of your friends.

Sally

Ben   Sunil

Ali   Gareth   Katie

Gallery

▶ Draw other people you know and label them.

Lollipop man   Dinner lady   My teacher

backspace

tap this key 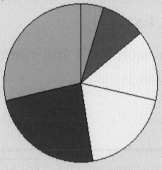 to rub out mistakes (called the Delete key on some machines).

cells

boxes in a spreadsheet.

click

quickly tapping the mouse.

data

information. It can be stored in a database.

document

a piece of work.

drag

to move something across the screen by pressing down on the mouse button.

field

a place in a database to store information.

folder

a place to keep your documents.

graph / chart

a way to show numbers as a picture:

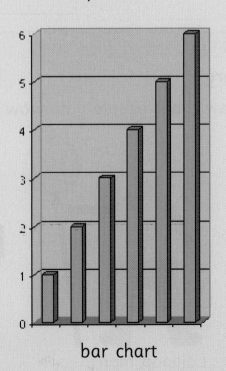

pie chart

bar chart

30

handles

squares round a shape:

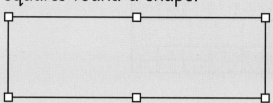

highlight

to select text or a graphic by clicking it, or dragging across it with the mouse.

icon

a picture you click on to make the computer do a particular job.

mouse

the tool you use to move a pointer  around the screen:

pointer

this shows where you are on the screen. It can have several different shapes:

spreadsheet

a place to store information in a grid of cells:

	A	B	C
1	Lee	9	
2	Sue	8	
3	Imran	8	
4	Dave	6	
5	Ralph	9	
6	Ricky	7	
7	Dan	8	
8	Shazia	7	
9	Laura	8	
10	Liz	12	
11			
12			

text box

a block of text you can drag with a mouse.

window

a small screen for writing and drawing in.

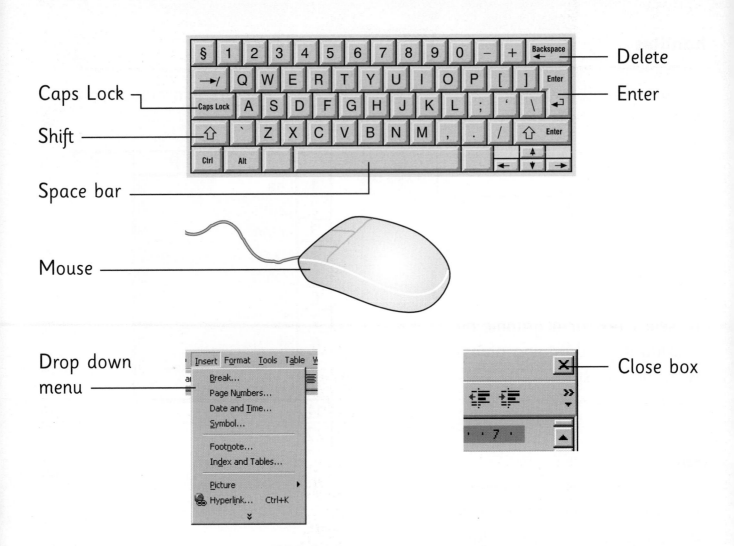

Delete

Caps Lock

Enter

Shift

Space bar

Mouse

Drop down menu

Close box

Menu toolbar

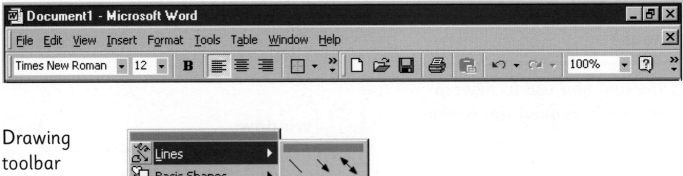

Drawing toolbar

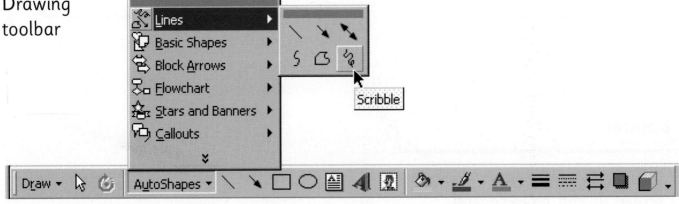